KENNY'S
BRIGHT RED SCOOTER

AMANDA KLINE
ILLUSTRATED BY JULIE BOURNE

NEW YORK

LONDON • NASHVILLE • MELBOURNE • VANCOUVER

KENNY'S BRIGHT RED SCOOTER

Published in New York, New York, by Morgan James Publishing. Morgan James is a trademark of Morgan James, LLC. www.MorganJamesPublishing.com

Proudly distributed by Publishers Group West®

A FREE ebook edition is available for you or a friend with the purchase of this print book.

CLEARLY SIGN YOUR NAME ABOVE

Instructions to claim your free ebook edition:
1. Visit MorganJamesBOGO.com
2. Sign your name CLEARLY in the space above
3. Complete the form and submit a photo of this entire page
4. You or your friend can download the ebook to your preferred device

ISBN 9781636981352 paperback
ISBN 9781636981369 ebook
Library of Congress Control Number: 2023931852

Cover and Interior Design by:
Julie Bourne

Morgan James is a proud partner of Habitat for Humanity Peninsula and Greater Williamsburg. Partners in building since 2006.

Get involved today! Visit: www.morgan-james-publishing.com/giving-back

For Aunt Debbie, Jenny, Jerry, and Kenny who have scooted with me through life. I can't imagine this beautiful journey without you. A2

For my mama, Jenny Sue Bourne, who was forever bringing home beautifully illustrated children's books and spending many delightful hours recreating these books' worlds in American Sign Language. J.B.

As a thank you to our active-duty service members and veterans, a portion of the proceeds from this book will be donated to the Patriotic Kenny Foundation.

As a boy, Kenny always dreamed of becoming a sailor, just like his Uncle Jimmy.

After graduating high school, he followed in his uncle's "boot steps" and joined the U.S. Navy.

Kenny worked on a large ship. He felt privileged to serve his country! He was friends with the sailors and he dreamed in red, white, and blue.

When he finished the Navy, he started a family. Soon after, his Uncle Jimmy passed away and was buried near home in Minnesota.

"One day, I'll put out flags to honor veterans," Kenny determined.

Kenny was busy for many years raising his family and building cars. After work, he'd drive by the cemetery.

"One day, I'll find time to put out flags, but not today. I'm too busy. My friends and family need me."

FORT SNELLING NATIONAL CEMETERY

Many years passed with Kenny serving others by listening to veterans and encouraging people at the coffee shop. He cared for every person he met.

Sadly, Kenny's health became worse.
Walking made it hard for him to breathe.
"One day, I'm afraid I won't be able
to walk to put out flags."

The next day, a grand thing happened.

Kenny spotted a garage sale near his home.
He slowly made his way to a red cushiony chair with wheels.

A mobility scooter for sale!

Kenny felt free zipping around on his bright red scooter!

He filled the air with smiles!

He scooted his way to the coffee shop.

He had no idea the next conversation would change his life.

Kenny strolled by two curly-haired women who asked, "Are you Kenny?!" "I am!" he replied.

"We've heard all about you!" Amanda exclaimed.

"It's a pleasure to know you!" Kenny beamed as his smile wrinkles grew.

He noticed Jenny was Deaf because she used her hands to talk. He also met Jenny's dad on video chat. He was Deaf, too!

From that moment, they formed The Crew:

Kenny, Amanda, Jenny, and Jerry.

The Crew loved spending time with veterans, learning sign language, and being in a July 4th parade!

Amanda shared videos with the world about Kenny spreading contagious joy during his scooter travels.

Kenny was finally ready to bring his scooter to the cemetery to place flags! But when Kenny's bright red scooter stopped working, that dream had to wait again.

The scooter would go, then stop. Go, then stop.
Until it stopped and wouldn't go anymore.

Kenny didn't have money to buy a new one.
"One day I'll put out flags, but not today."

Amanda shared a video
about his broken scooter.
Millions of people watched
the video!

People from all over the world
donated money to help Kenny.

He could buy a new bright red scooter!

Kenny sobbed, "No, you're kidding!!"

Kenny got his NEW scooter,
and of course, it had to be RED!

He knew what he needed to do.

On Memorial Day, the cemetery had a special event to remember veterans who weren't alive anymore. People could volunteer to put out flags by the veteran graves. Kenny had waited his whole life for this and nothing would stop him this time.

"Long ago, I said I'd honor veterans with flags, and that day is finally today!"

The sky dropped light rain tears that morning.

The Crew got hundreds of flags. Kenny's scooter respectfully led him to the sea of white headstones.

He gasped back tears at the first veteran's grave and saluted.

His wrinkled hand proudly pushed the red, white, and blue flag into American soil

with Kennyheartedness.

The Crew paused with each flag to remember
the people who sacrificed for America.

Kenny's scooter flags flapped in the breeze as
he set his eyes on one far-away grave.

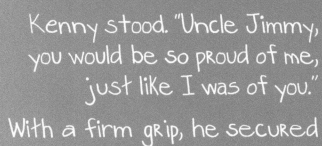

Kenny stood. "Uncle Jimmy,
you would be so proud of me,
just like I was of you."

With a firm grip, he secured
the flag into the ground.
He snapped a crisp salute and cried,
"Thank you for your service, Uncle Jim."

The Crew placed flags every year,
but they wanted to continue showing
kindness to veterans.

They decided to give away many
bright red scooters to deserving
veterans in need.

To show Kindness to others, the Crew has also given flowers to veterans in nursing homes, left quarters in gumball machines, and taped money to gas pumps.

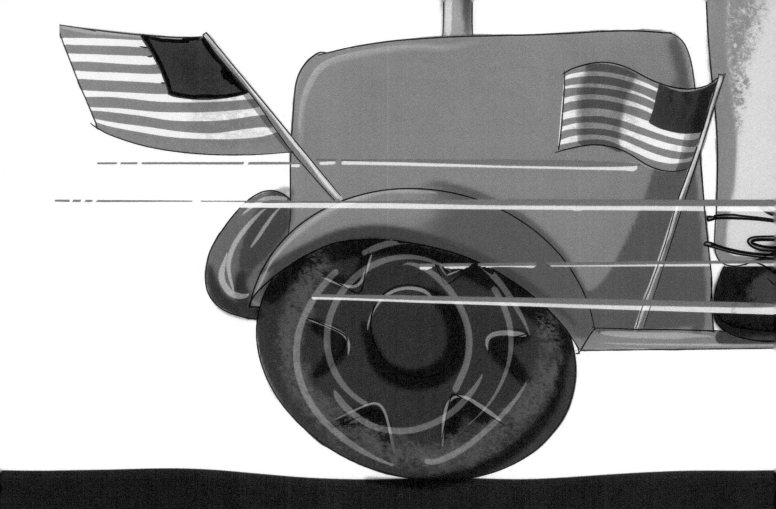

Everywhere we go we have opportunities to be sensitive to others and to be a friend.

Try sharing a smile with someone today.

. . . and if you see a bright red scooter with
flags stroll by, make sure to say hello.

You never know how a simple act of kindness
could change their world.

MILITARY BRANCHES

ARMY

The Army fights on land for freedom.

AIR FORCE

The Air Force fights in the air to defend America.

SPACE FORCE

The Space Force protects space for the United States. They work with the Air Force.

COAST GUARD

The Coast Guard ensures people and ships are safe and follow the rules at sea.

MARINES

The Marines protect by land, sea, and air. They work with the Navy.

NAVY

The Navy protects on, under, and over the sea.

ABOUT PATRIOTIC KENNY

Kenny Jary, affectionately known as Patriotic Kenny, is a friendly senior citizen Navy veteran who was born and raised in St. Paul, Minnesota. He proudly served in the Navy from 1959-1965 as a plankowner aboard his ship, the USS Okinawa which was stationed out of Norfolk, Virginia. He was deployed to San Juan, Puerto Rico during the Cuban Missile Crisis. Kenny has the utmost respect for our country's servicemembers.

Due to a chronic lung condition, Kenny uses the help of a mobility scooter to get around and to spread joy! When his friend and neighbor, Amanda, discovered his mobility scooter was broken and he couldn't afford a new one, she set up a GoFundMe on his TikTok channel, @patriotickenny. Within one day, people from all over the world donated $5,000 to Kenny! Within a week, people donated over $100,000!

As a way to pay it forward, Kenny and the Crew have been giving back mobility scooters to veterans and founded the Patriotic Kenny Foundation to empower and honor veterans through mobility wellness.

Learn more and get involved to show kindness at www.patriotickenny.com.

ABOUT THE AUTHOR

Amanda Kline founded the viral social media account, @patrioticKenny on TikTok & Instagram and has been featured with Kenny on *The Today Show*, *Kelly Clarkson*, *Newsweek*, *GoFundMe Heroes*, and many others. She is a reading & writing teacher to Deaf middle school students and is also a Ph.D. student at Gallaudet University.

Amanda has abundant love for social media, senior citizens, and veterans. She enjoys hobbies of all sorts such as video editing, drinking coffee, and donating mobility scooters. When not hanging out with the Crew, she often relaxes at one of the 14,380 lakes at home in Minnesota. This is her debut book.

ABOUT THE ILLUSTRATOR

Julie Bourne is a Deaf illustrator and owner of her design services firm, Flowbird Design Solutions. Bourne holds a master's degree in project management from George Washington University and has more than 20 years of experience in finance and education. Most recently, she taught photography, graphic design, and computer science to Deaf students.

Bourne lives in Maryland with four most lovely and lively children (one of them ten pounds and furry) and a wonderfully supportive husband. Kenny's Bright Red Scooter is her first book.

A free ebook edition is available with the purchase of this book.

To claim your free ebook edition:

1. Visit MorganJamesBOGO.com
2. Sign your name CLEARLY in the space
3. Complete the form and submit a photo of the entire copyright page
4. You or your friend can download the ebook to your preferred device

Print & Digital Together Forever.

Snap a photo

Free ebook

Read anywhere

View this book in American Sign Language
and get free resources at

www.amandaKline.com

CPSIA information can be obtained
at www.ICGtesting.com
Printed in the USA
JSHW040056130523
41683JS00001B/1

9 781636 981352